**KS2 9–10 Years**

## Master Maths at Home

# Fractions, Decimals and Percentage

Scan the QR code to help your child's learning at home.

mastermathsathome.com

# How to use this book

**Maths — No Problem!** created **Master Maths at Home** to help children develop fluency in the subject and a rich understanding of core concepts.

**Key features of the Master Maths at Home books include:**

- Carefully designed lessons that provide structure, but also allow flexibility in how they're used.

- Speech bubbles containing content designed to spark diverse conversations, with many discussion points that don't have obvious 'right' or 'wrong' answers.

- Rich illustrations that will guide children to a discussion of shapes and units of measurement, allowing them to make connections to the wider world around them.

- Exercises that allow a flexible approach and can be adapted to suit any child's cognitive or functional ability.

- Clearly laid-out pages that encourage children to practise a range of higher-order skills.

- A community of friendly and relatable characters who introduce each lesson and come along as your child progresses through the series.

You can see more guidance on how to use these books at mastermathsathome.com.

We're excited to share all the ways you can learn maths!

---

Copyright © 2022 Maths — No Problem!

Maths — No Problem!
mastermathsathome.com
www.mathsnoproblem.com
hello@mathsnoproblem.com

First published in Great Britain in 2022 by
Dorling Kindersley Limited
One Embassy Gardens, 8 Viaduct Gardens, London SW11 7BW
A Penguin Random House Company

The authorised representative in the EEA is Dorling Kindersley Verlag GmbH. Arnulfstr. 124, 80636 Munich, Germany

10 9 8 7 6 5 4 3 2 1
001–327099–May/22

This book was made with Forest Stewardship Council™ certified paper - one small step in DK's commitment to a sustainable future. For more information go to www.dk.com/our-green-pledge

All rights reserved. Without limiting the rights under the copyright reserved above, no part of this publication may be reproduced, stored in, or introduced into a retrieval system, or transmitted, in any form, or by any means (electronic, mechanical, photocopying, recording, or otherwise), without the prior written permission of the copyright owner.

A CIP catalogue record for this book is available from the British Library.

ISBN: 978-0-24153-944-6
Printed and bound in the UK

For the curious
www.dk.com

**Acknowledgements**
The publisher would like to thank the authors and consultants Andy Psarianos, Judy Hornigold, Adam Gifford and Dr Anne Hermanson.

The Castledown typeface has been used with permission from the Colophon Foundry.

# Contents

| | Page |
|---|---|
| Dividing to make fractions | 4 |
| Mixed numbers | 6 |
| Improper fractions | 8 |
| Converting improper fractions to mixed numbers | 10 |
| Converting mixed numbers to improper fractions | 12 |
| Equivalent fractions | 14 |
| More equivalent fractions | 16 |
| Comparing fractions | 18 |
| Fractions of quantities | 20 |
| Adding fractions | 24 |
| Subtracting fractions | 26 |
| Multiplying fractions | 28 |
| Comparing fractions using decimals | 30 |
| Adding and subtracting decimals | 32 |
| Rounding decimals | 34 |
| Percentages | 36 |
| Review and challenge | 40 |
| Answers | 46 |

# Dividing to make fractions

**Lesson 1**

## Starter

Four friends want to share 3 pizzas equally. How much pizza will each friend get?

## Example

When we share we use division. 3 pizzas shared between 4 friends is written as 3 ÷ 4.

Each friend will get less than 1 pizza.

To share the pizzas we can cut each pizza into 4 equal pieces.

Each friend gets 3 quarters of a pizza.

$3 ÷ 4 = \dfrac{3}{4}$

# Practice

**1** Divide.

(a) $2 \div 5 = \dfrac{\Box}{\Box}$

(b) $2 \div 4 = \dfrac{\Box}{\Box}$

**2** Look at the pictures and fill in the blanks.

(a) Two circles are shaded equally in 3 different colours. How much of the circles are shaded in each colour?

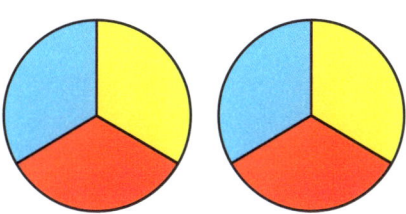

$2 \div 3 = \dfrac{\Box}{\Box}$

$\dfrac{\Box}{\Box}$ of the circles are shaded in each colour.

(b) Four candy strips are shared by 6 friends. How much of a candy strip does each friend get?

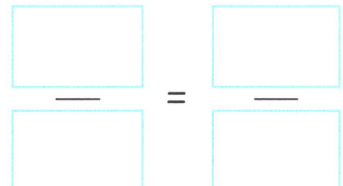

$\dfrac{\Box}{\Box} = \dfrac{\Box}{\Box}$

Each friend gets $\dfrac{\Box}{\Box}$ of a candy strip.

# Mixed numbers

Lesson 2

## Starter

How much of the hexagons are shaded yellow?

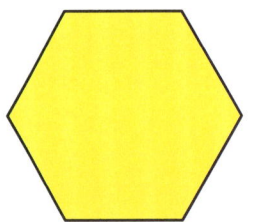 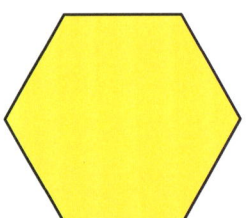 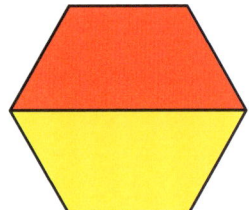

## Example

This shape has 6 sides. It is called a hexagon.

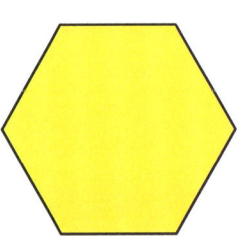

Each hexagon is 1 whole. There are 2 whole hexagons shaded yellow.

There is also 1 half of a hexagon shaded yellow.

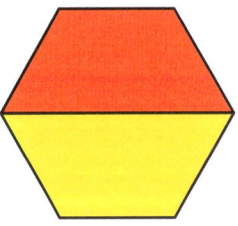

2 whole hexagons and 1 half of a hexagon makes 2 and 1 half hexagons.

There are $2\frac{1}{2}$ hexagons shaded yellow.

When we write a number using whole numbers and fractions we call these **mixed numbers**.

# Practice

Answer the questions using a mixed number.

**1** How much of the squares are shaded orange?

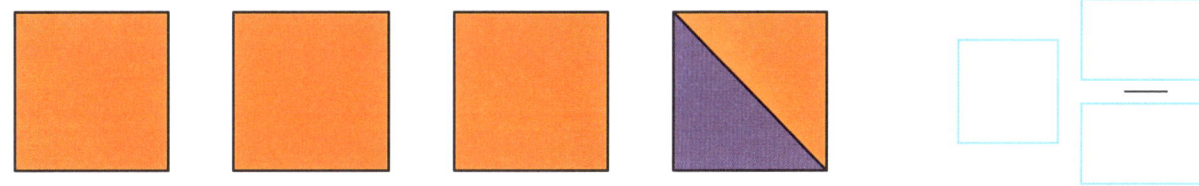

**2** How much of the hexagons are shaded yellow?

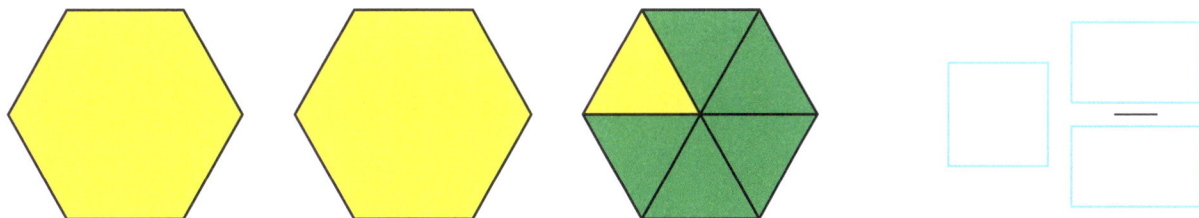

**3** How much of the hexagons are shaded yellow?

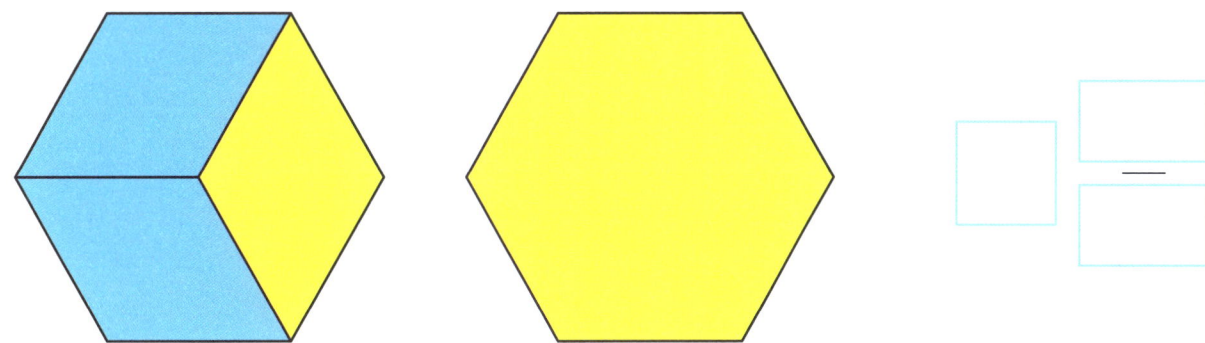

**4** How much of the rhombuses are shaded blue?

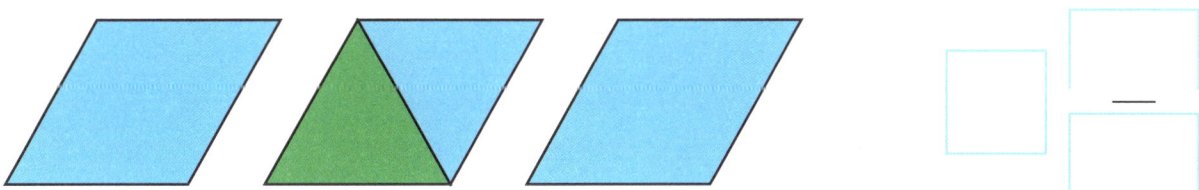

# Improper fractions

**Lesson 3**

## Starter

Amira is baking orange fairy cakes for her sister's birthday party. Each batch of fairy cakes needs the juice from $\frac{1}{2}$ of an orange.

Amira needs to make 5 batches for the party.
How many oranges does she need for the 5 batches of fairy cakes?

## Example

Each batch needs the juice from $\frac{1}{2}$ of an orange.

There are 5 batches. Amira needs the juice from 5 half oranges.

$$\frac{1}{2} + \frac{1}{2} + \frac{1}{2} + \frac{1}{2} + \frac{1}{2} = \frac{5}{2}$$

We can write it as $\frac{5}{2}$.

When a fraction has a numerator equal to or greater than the denominator it is called an improper fraction.

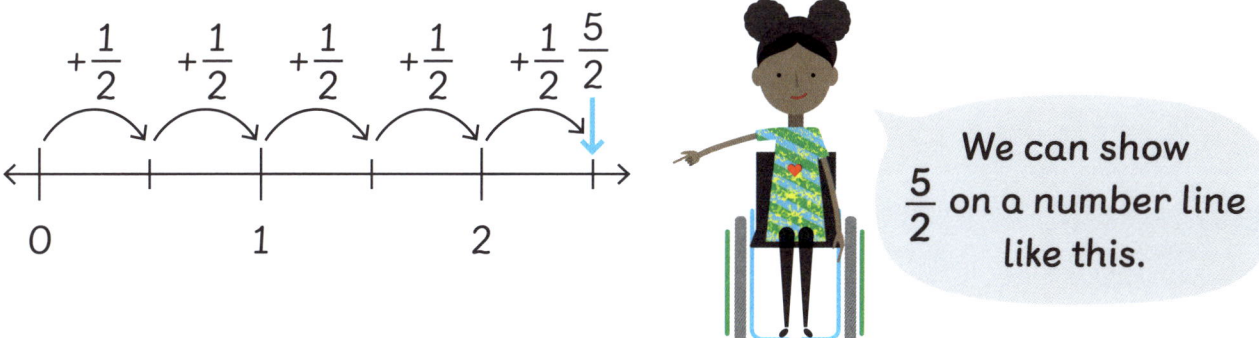

Amira needs $\frac{5}{2}$ oranges for the 5 batches of fairy cakes.

## Practice

Give your answers as improper fractions.

**1** (a) How many half bananas are there?

(b) How many quarters of pancake are there?

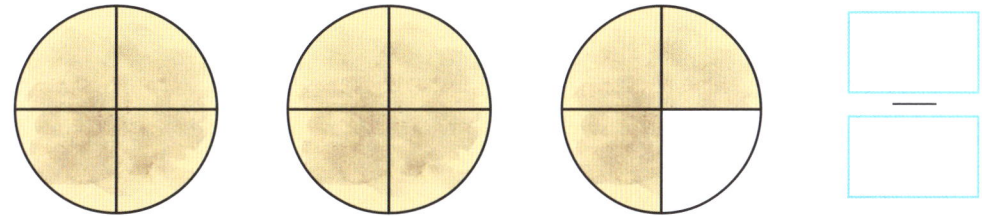

**2** Fill in the blanks.

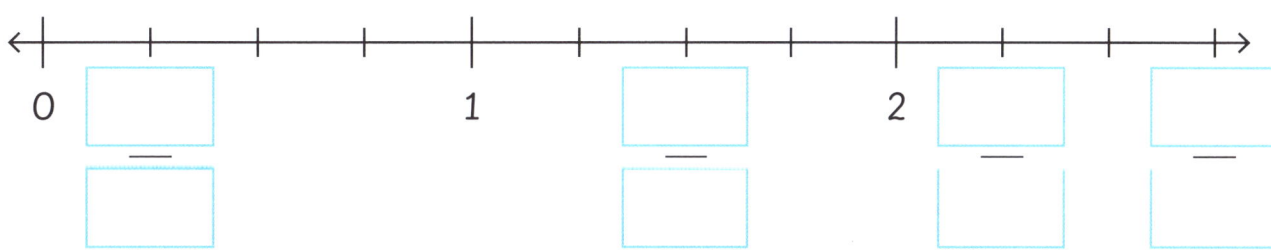

# Converting improper fractions to mixed numbers

**Lesson 4**

## Starter

Each rhombus is $\frac{1}{3}$ of a hexagon.

These shapes are called rhombuses. Each side of a rhombus is the same length.

How many hexagons can we make with these rhombuses?

## Example

I can arrange 3  like this to make a hexagon.

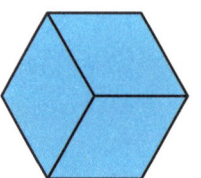

There are 11 .
Each  is $\frac{1}{3}$ of a hexagon.
There are 11 thirds of a hexagon in total.

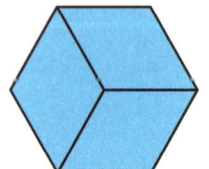   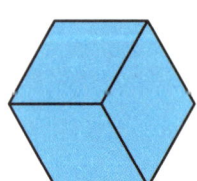   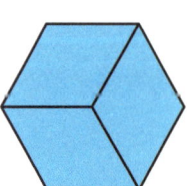   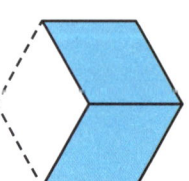

   1           1           1           $\frac{2}{3}$

$\frac{11}{3} = 3\frac{2}{3}$

I can make 3 whole hexagons. I have 2 thirds left over.

We can make $3\frac{2}{3}$ hexagons from the 11 rhombuses.

# Practice

**1** Read the questions and fill in the blanks.

(a) Each semi-circle is 1 half of a circle.
How many circles can you make using the semi-circles?

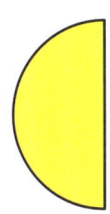   

There are ☐ semi-circles.

$\dfrac{\square}{2} = \square \dfrac{\square}{\square}$

(b) Each triangle is 1 half of a square.
How many squares can you make using the triangles?

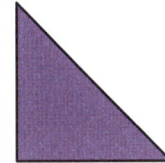 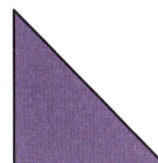   

There are ☐ triangles.

$\dfrac{\square}{2} = \square \dfrac{\square}{\square}$

**2** Fill in the blanks.

(a) $\dfrac{27}{12} = \square \dfrac{\square}{\square}$

(b) $1\dfrac{7}{11} = \dfrac{\square}{\square}$

# Converting mixed numbers to improper fractions

**Lesson 5**

## Starter

A bakery assistant cuts each cake into 6 slices. How many slices of cake can the bakery assistant get altogether after cutting the whole cakes?

## Example

There are 3 whole cakes. Each cake is cut into 6 slices. Each slice is $\frac{1}{6}$ of a cake.

There are also 5 slices left. The 5 slices are $\frac{5}{6}$ of a cake.

   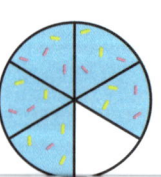

$\frac{6}{6}$   $\frac{6}{6}$   $\frac{6}{6}$   $\frac{5}{6}$

$3\frac{5}{6}$ is equal to $\frac{23}{6}$.

The bakery assistant can get 23 slices of cake altogether after cutting the whole cakes.

# Practice

**1** Fill in the blanks.

(a)
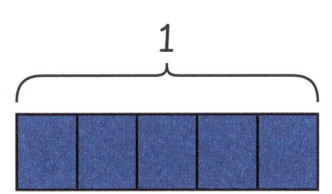
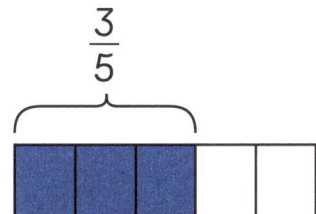

$1\frac{3}{5} = \frac{\boxed{\phantom{0}}}{5}$

(b)

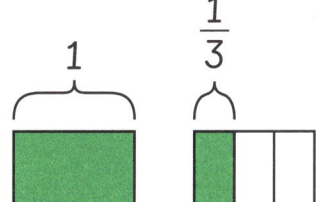

$3\frac{1}{3} = \frac{\boxed{\phantom{0}}}{3}$

(c)

$\boxed{\phantom{0}} \frac{\boxed{\phantom{0}}}{4} = \frac{\boxed{\phantom{0}}}{4}$

**2** Ravi cuts each hexagon into 6 identical triangles.
He starts with 5 hexagons and 1 triangle.
How many triangles does he end up with?

 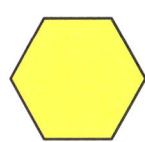 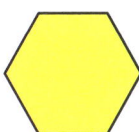 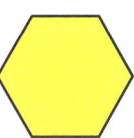 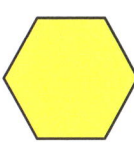 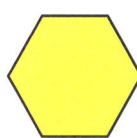

$5\frac{1}{6} = \frac{\boxed{\phantom{0}}}{6}$

Ravi ends up with $\boxed{\phantom{0}}$ triangles.

# Equivalent fractions

Lesson 6

## Starter

Sam and Emma both ordered a pizza for lunch. Who has more pizza left?

I cut my pizza into 4 equal pieces and I ate 2 of the pieces.

I cut my pizza into 2 equal pieces and I ate 1 piece.

## Example

 Sam and Emma each started with a whole pizza.

 Sam cut his pizza into 4 quarters and Emma cut her pizza into 2 halves.

 Emma has 1 piece of pizza left. Sam has 2 pieces of pizza left.

$\frac{1}{2}$   $\frac{2}{4}$

1 quarter of a pizza is less than 1 half of a pizza. 2 quarters of a pizza is the same amount as 1 half of a pizza.

 When different fractions have the same value we say that they are **equivalent fractions**. $\frac{1}{2}$ and $\frac{2}{4}$ are equivalent fractions.

Sam and Emma both have the same amount of pizza left.

# Practice

Fill in the blanks to show the equivalent fractions.

**1**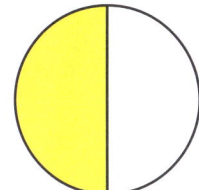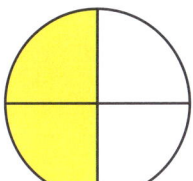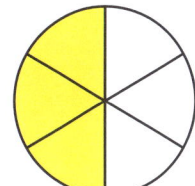

$$\frac{1}{2} = \frac{\square}{4} = \frac{3}{\square} = \frac{\square}{8}$$

**2**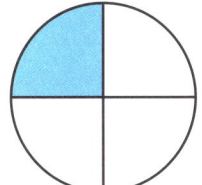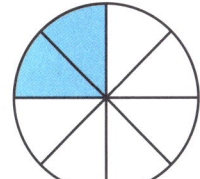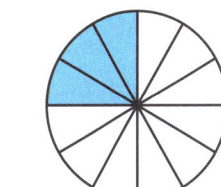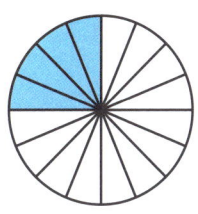

$$\frac{1}{4} = \frac{2}{\square} = \frac{3}{\square} = \frac{\square}{16}$$

**3**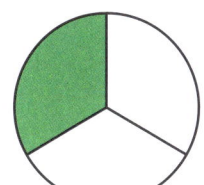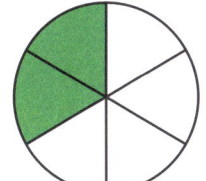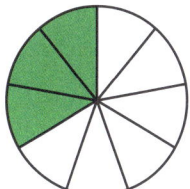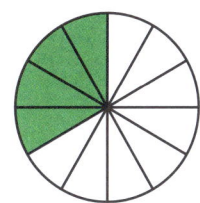

$$\frac{1}{3} = \frac{2}{\square} = \frac{3}{\square} = \frac{\square}{\square}$$

**4**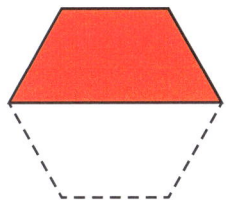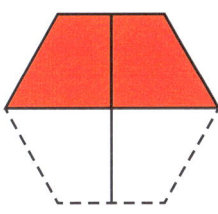

$$\frac{1}{2} = \frac{\square}{4}$$

15

# More equivalent fractions

**Lesson 7**

## Starter

I can find equivalent fractions by multiplying the numerator and denominator by the same number.

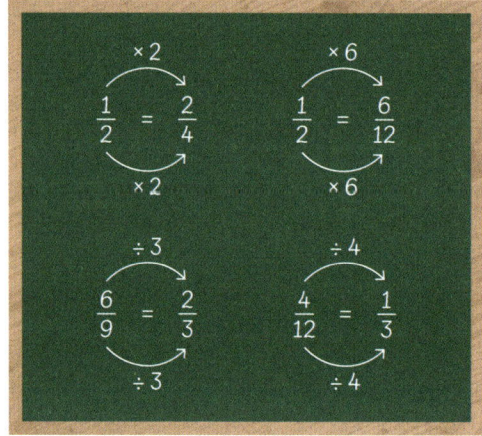

I can find equivalent fractions by dividing them by the same number.

Are Lulu and Holly both correct?

## Example

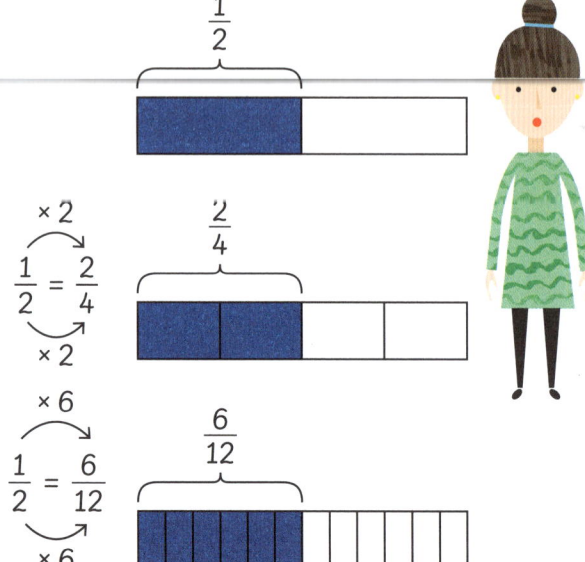

We can check using bar models.

When I multiply the numerator and denominator by the same number the fractions are equivalent.

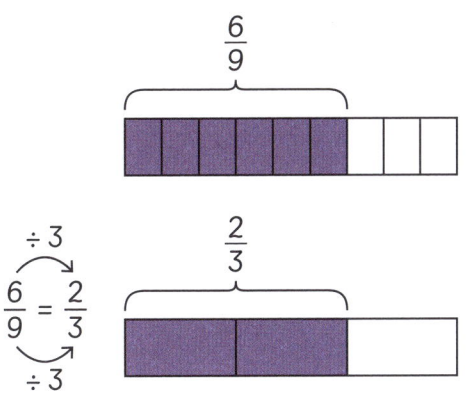

It also works when you divide the numerator and denominator by the same number. The fractions are equivalent.

When we divide the numerator and denominator by the same number we call it **simplifying** the fraction.

Both Lulu and Holly are correct.

## Practice

Match the equivalent fractions.

$\frac{6}{12}$ •

$\frac{15}{20}$ •

$\frac{8}{12}$ •    • $\frac{2}{3}$

$\frac{10}{15}$ •    • $\frac{3}{4}$

$\frac{9}{12}$ •    • $\frac{1}{2}$

$\frac{5}{10}$ •

# Comparing fractions

**Lesson 8**

## Starter

Oak and Ruby are collecting pictures for a school art project. They each need to collect 200 pictures.

I have $\frac{5}{8}$ of my 200 pictures.

I have $\frac{7}{10}$ of my pictures.

Who has collected more pictures?

## Example

We can use bar models. First, we draw a bar for Oak to represent 200 pictures. Next, we split it into 8 equal parts to make eighths. We can then show $\frac{5}{8}$ of the bar.

We can do the same for Ruby, but we need to split the bar into 10 equal parts to show $\frac{7}{10}$.

If we compare the bar models, we can see that Ruby has collected more pictures. $\frac{7}{10}$ of 200 pictures is more than $\frac{5}{8}$ of 200 pictures.

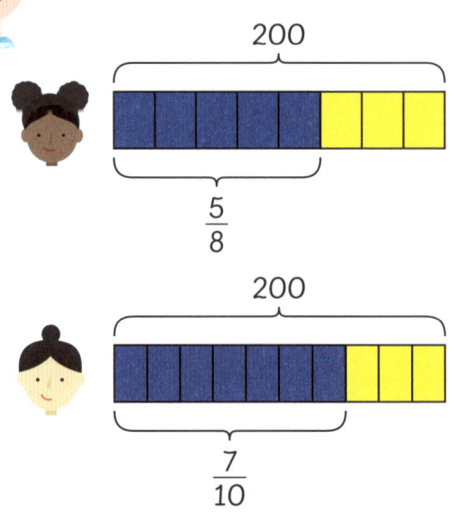

Both numbers are more than $\frac{1}{2}$ and less than 1. I can show them on number lines. $\frac{5}{8}$ is closer to $\frac{1}{2}$ and $\frac{7}{10}$ is closer to 1.

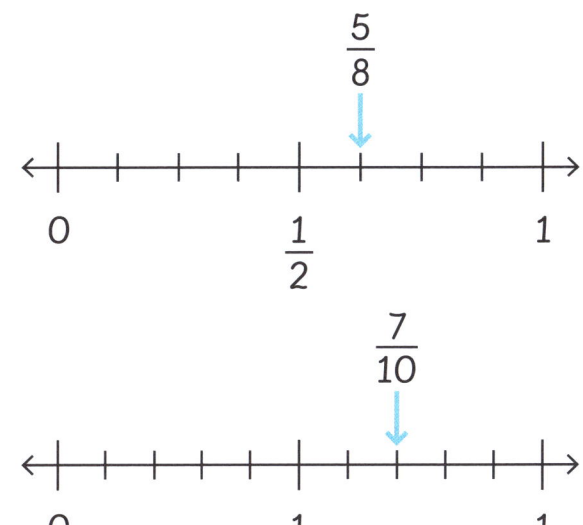

$\frac{7}{10} > \frac{5}{8}$

Ruby has collected more pictures than Oak has collected.

## Practice

Charles, Emma and Elliott need to read the same book for homework. Charles has finished $\frac{5}{6}$ of the book. Emma has read $\frac{6}{7}$ of the book. Elliott has read $\frac{5}{8}$ of the book.

**1** Shade the bar models to show how much of the book each child has read.

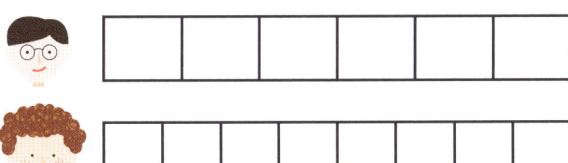

**2** Fill in the blanks with **most, more, less** or **least**.as read.

Charles has read ☐ than Emma.

Emma has read ☐ than Elliott.

Elliott has read ☐ than Charles.

Emma has the ☐ number of pages left to read.

**3** ☐ has read the most and ☐ has read the least.

# Fractions of quantities

Lesson 9

## Starter

Oak and Ruby continue collecting pictures for a school art project. They each need to collect 200 pictures.

How many more pictures do each of them need to collect?

## Example

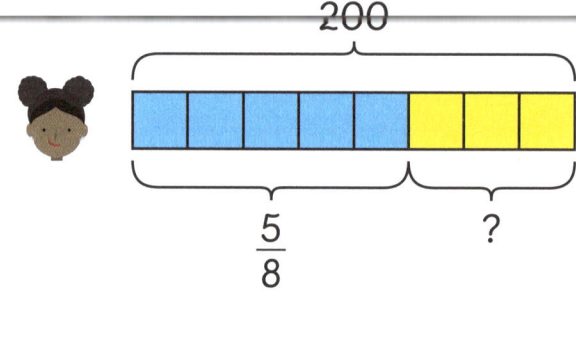

We now need to find how many pictures each of them still has to collect. Let's start with Oak.

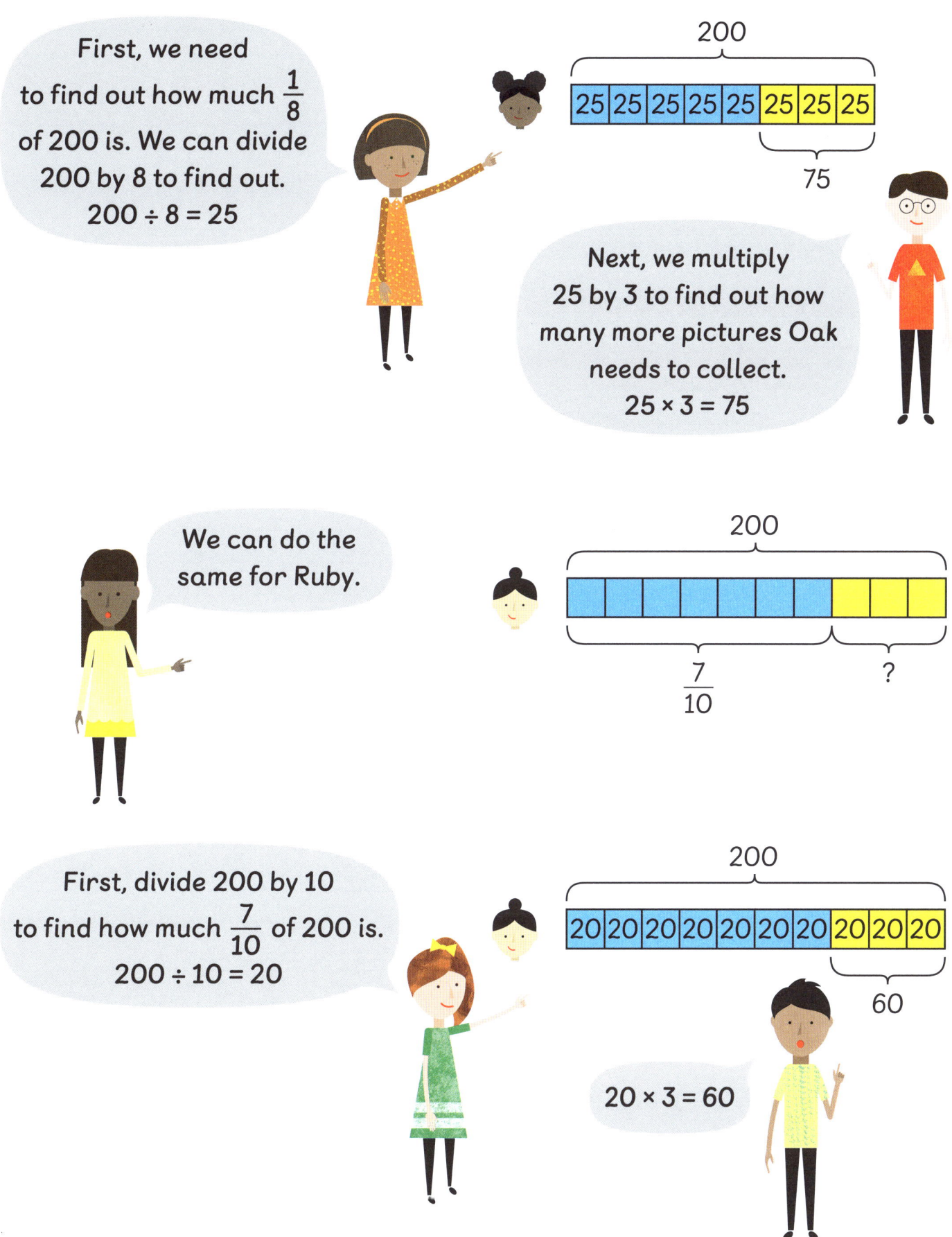

Oak still needs to collect 75 pictures and Ruby still needs to collect 60 pictures.

# Practice

**1** Solve.

Hannah scored 150 points in her video game.
Lulu scored $\frac{2}{3}$ as many points as Hannah scored.

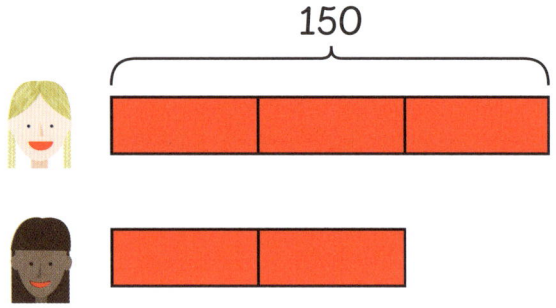

(a) How many points did Lulu score?

Lulu scored [ ] points.

(b) How many points did Hannah and Lulu score altogether?

Hannah and Lulu scored [ ] points altogether.

**2** Draw a bar model to solve each question and fill in the blanks.

Ravi's older brother needs to save £180 so he can go on the rugby trip with his team.
So far he has saved $\frac{3}{5}$ of £180.

(a) How much has Ravi's brother saved so far?

180 ÷ ☐ = ☐

☐ × 3 = ☐

So far Ravi's brother has saved £ ☐.

(b) Ravi's brother's teammate has saved $\frac{5}{6}$ as much as Ravi's brother has saved so far.
How much has his teammate saved?

☐ ÷ 6 = ☐

☐ × ☐ = ☐

His teammate has saved £ ☐.

# Adding fractions

Lesson 10

## Starter

Amira and her mum are on a hike together.

Amira has $\frac{3}{4}$ l of water left in her container.

Amira's mum has $\frac{1}{2}$ l of water left in her containers.

How much water do they have in total?

## Example

 We need to add $\frac{1}{2}$ to $\frac{3}{4}$.

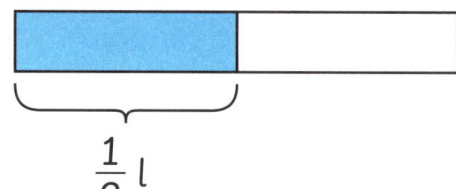

$\frac{1}{2}$ l

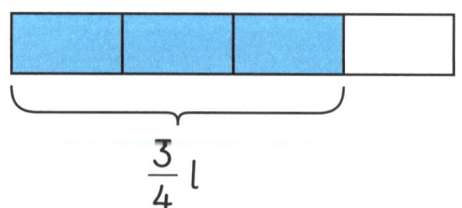

$\frac{3}{4}$ l

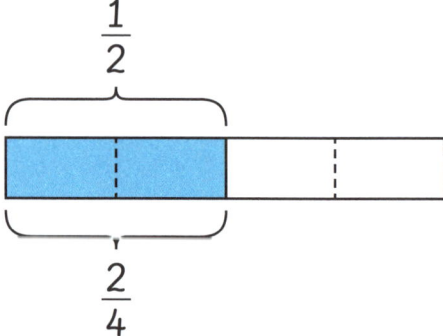

$\frac{1}{2}$

$\frac{2}{4}$

 Both fractions need to have the same denominator before we can add them. One half is equal to 2 quarters.

24

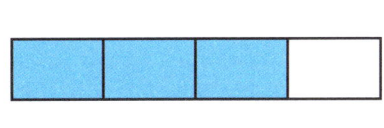  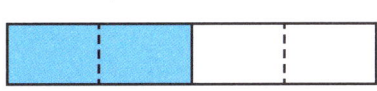  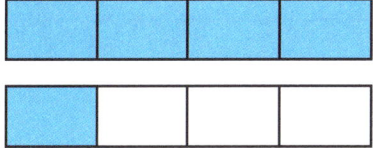

$\frac{3}{4}$ + $\frac{2}{4}$ = $1\frac{1}{4}$

Amira and her mum have $1\frac{1}{4}$ l of water in total.

$\frac{3}{4} + \frac{2}{4} = \frac{5}{4}$

$\frac{5}{4} = 1\frac{1}{4}$

## Practice

Shade the bar models and fill in the blanks.

**1**

$\frac{3}{8}$ + $\frac{4}{8}$ = $\frac{\square}{\square}$

**2**

$\frac{1}{4}$ + $\frac{1}{2}$ = $\frac{\square}{\square}$

**3**

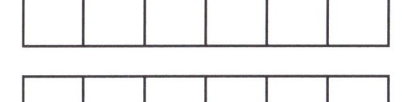

$\frac{2}{3}$ + $\frac{5}{6}$ =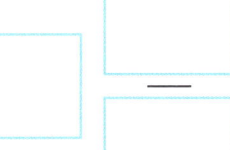

# Subtracting fractions

**Lesson 11**

## Starter

A restaurant has $1\frac{1}{2}$ kg of rice in the pantry at the beginning of the day. It uses $\frac{5}{8}$ kg of the rice by the middle of the day.

How much rice does the restaurant now have left?

## Example

We need to subtract $\frac{5}{8}$ from $1\frac{1}{2}$.

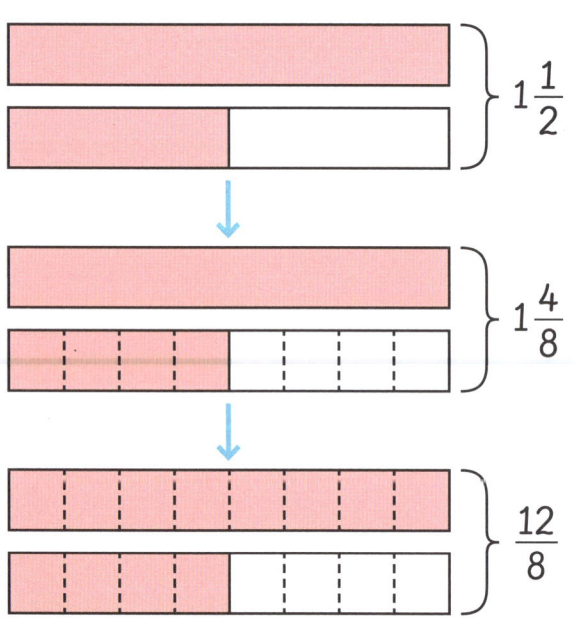

We can't subtract fractions with different denominators. We can't easily change $\frac{5}{8}$ to halves but we can change $\frac{1}{2}$ to eighths easily.

$$\frac{1}{2} \underset{\times 4}{\overset{\times 4}{=}} \frac{4}{8}$$

In order to subtract $\frac{5}{8}$ we can convert $1\frac{4}{8}$ to an improper fraction.

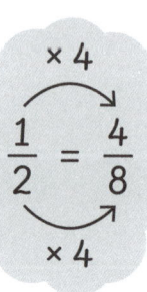

We can subtract 5 eighths from 12 eighths.

$$\frac{12}{8} - \frac{5}{8} = \frac{7}{8}$$

We can also show it on a number line.

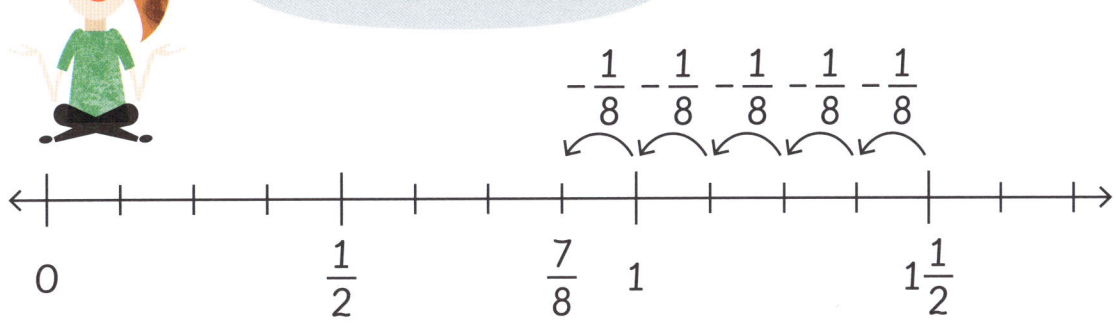

The restaurant now has $\frac{7}{8}$ kg of rice left.

## Practice

**1** Match the equations with the images.

$1\frac{3}{4} - \frac{7}{8} = \frac{7}{8}$

$1\frac{3}{5} - \frac{7}{10} = \frac{9}{10}$

$\frac{2}{3} - \frac{1}{6} = \frac{1}{2}$

**2** Fill in the blanks.

(a) $\frac{3}{4} - \frac{1}{2} = \frac{\square}{\square} - \frac{\square}{\square} = \frac{\square}{\square}$

(b) $1\frac{2}{3} - \frac{5}{6} = \frac{\square}{\square} - \frac{5}{6} = \frac{\square}{\square}$

# Multiplying fractions

**Lesson 12**

## Starter

Jacob finds an old cake recipe in his grandmother's kitchen.

The recipe says to use $\frac{3}{4}$ lb of butter for each cake. He wants to bake 3 cakes for the school fete. How much butter does Jacob need to bake 3 cakes?

1 lb means 1 pound. 1 lb is equal to 454 g.

## Example

We can use multiplication to find out. Each cake needs $\frac{3}{4}$ lb of butter. Jacob needs 3 × 3 quarter lb of butter.

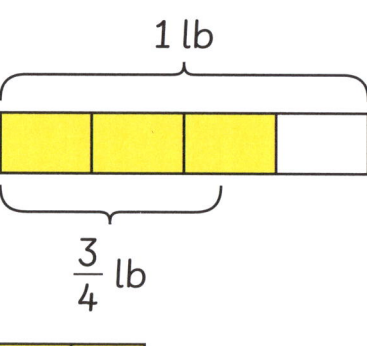

1 lb

$\frac{3}{4}$ lb

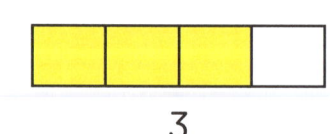
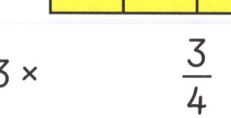

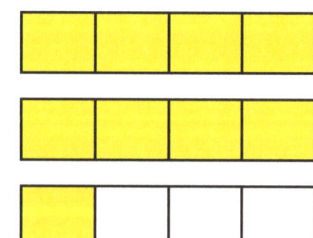

$3 \times \quad \frac{3}{4} \quad = \quad \frac{9}{4} \quad = \quad 2\frac{1}{4}$

3 × 3 quarter lb of butter is equal to 9 quarter lb of butter.

We can show $\frac{9}{4}$ as a mixed number. $\frac{9}{4}$ is equal to $2\frac{1}{4}$.

$3 \times \frac{3}{4} = \frac{9}{4} = 2\frac{1}{4}$

Jacob needs $2\frac{1}{4}$ lb of butter to bake 3 cakes.

# Practice

Shade the bar models and fill in the blanks.
The first one has been shaded for you.

**1**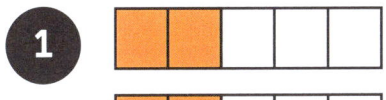

$2 \times \dfrac{2}{5} = \dfrac{\boxed{\phantom{0}}}{5}$

**2**

$3 \times \dfrac{2}{3} = \boxed{\phantom{0}}$

**3**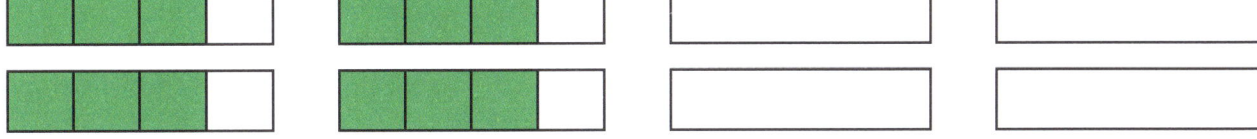

$\boxed{\phantom{0}} \times \dfrac{\boxed{\phantom{0}}}{\boxed{\phantom{0}}} = \boxed{\phantom{0}}$

# Comparing fractions using decimals

**Lesson 13**

## Starter

Elliott needs to order these numbers from smallest to greatest. What order should he put them in?

$\frac{6}{10}$

$\frac{1}{2}$

$\frac{45}{100}$

$\frac{535}{1000}$

## Example

We can convert the fractions to decimals to help us.

$\frac{6}{10}$ = 0.1 0.1 0.1 0.1 0.1 0.1 = 0.6

Before we can convert $\frac{1}{2}$ to a decimal, we need to convert halves to tenths, hundredths or thousandths.

$\frac{5}{10}$ = 0.1 0.1 0.1 0.1 0.1 = 0.5

×5
$\frac{1}{2} = \frac{5}{10}$
×5

10 ×  is equal to 1 × .

$\frac{55}{100}$ = 0.1 0.1 0.01 0.01 0.1 0.1 0.01 0.01 0.1 0.01 = 0.55

 10 × 0.001 is equal to 1 × 0.01.

$\frac{535}{100}$ =  = 0.535

0.5 < 0.55
0.5 < 0.6
0.5 < 0.535
0.5 is the smallest number.

0.6 > 0.5
0.6 > 0.55
0.6 > 0.535
0.6 is the greatest number.

0.535 > $\frac{55}{100}$

| 0.5 | 0.535 | 0.55 | 0.6 |
| $\frac{1}{2}$ | $\frac{535}{1000}$ | $\frac{55}{100}$ | $\frac{6}{10}$ |

smallest →  greatest

## Practice

Convert the fractions to decimals and then put them in order from smallest to greatest.

 1. $\frac{2}{5}$ = ☐          $\frac{1}{2}$ = ☐          $\frac{38}{100}$ = ☐

☐ , ☐ , ☐

smallest → greatest

 2. $\frac{607}{1000}$ = ☐          $\frac{6}{100}$ = ☐          $\frac{6}{10}$ = ☐

☐ , ☐ , ☐

smallest → greatest

# Adding and subtracting decimals

**Lesson 14**

## Starter

Lulu went on a hike with her family. They hiked 3.6 km before stopping for lunch. They then hiked another 2.67 km in the afternoon.
How far did they hike in total that day?
How much further did they hike in the morning than in the afternoon?

## Example

We can add 3.6 to 2.67 to find out how far Lulu and her family hiked that day.

$$\begin{array}{r} \overset{1}{3}.6\phantom{0} \\ +\ 2.67 \\ \hline 6.27 \end{array}$$

We can use column addition and column subtraction but we need to be careful to line up the places correctly.

We need to subtract to find the difference.

3.60 is the same as 3.6.

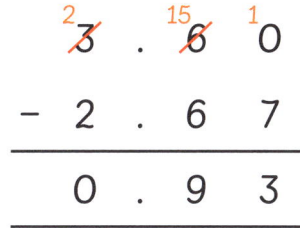

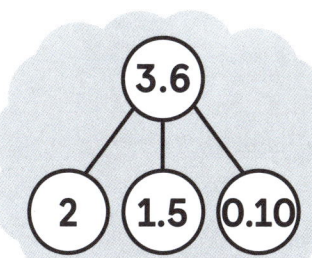

Lulu and her family hiked 6.27 km in total that day.
They hiked 0.93 km further in the morning than in the afternoon.

## Practice

1. Add.

   (a)   7 . 5 3
       + 6 . 2 3
       ─────────

   (b)   3 . 2 8
       + 4 . 5 3
       ─────────

   (c)   5 . 5 4
       + 4 . 3 6
       ─────────

   (d)   9 . 5 6
       + 9 . 4 4
       ─────────

   (e) 5.72 + 3 = ☐

   (f) 0.83 + 0.18 = ☐

2. Subtract.

   (a)   2 . 7 2
       − 1 . 3 3
       ─────────

   (b)   8 . 2 4
       − 3 . 5 5
       ─────────

   (c) 3.15 − 0.2 = ☐

   (d) 5 − 1.12 = ☐

# Rounding decimals

**Lesson 15**

## Starter

In a science class, Miss Fathima showed the children how to use a micrometer to measure the thickness of some items. The children found these measurements.

Sheet of paper from textbook: 0.183 mm
Textbook cover: 0.345 mm
Textbook: 11.276 mm
Plywood: 6.348 mm

How can we round the thickness of each item to the closest tenth and hundredth of a millimetre?

A micrometer is a device used to measure the thickness of objects very precisely.

## Example

We can show all the numbers on number lines.

0.183

0.1  0.11 0.12 0.13 0.14 0.15 0.16 0.17 0.18 0.19  0.2

Rounded to the closest:

| | hundredths | tenths |
|---|---|---|
| 0.183 | 0.18 | 0.2 |

0.345

0.3  0.31 0.32 0.33 0.34 0.35 0.36 0.37 0.38 0.39  0.4

Rounded to the closest:

| | hundredths | tenths |
|---|---|---|
| 0.345 | 0.35 | 0.3 |

34

| | Rounded to the closest: | |
|---|---|---|
| | hundredths | tenths |
| 11.276 | 11.28 | 11.3 |

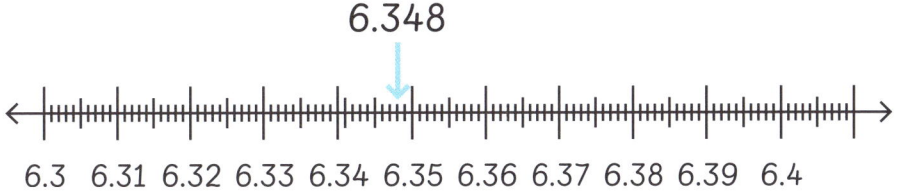

| | Rounded to the closest: | |
|---|---|---|
| | hundredths | tenths |
| 6.348 | 6.35 | 6.3 |

## Practice

Show the numbers on the number lines and fill in the blanks.

**1**

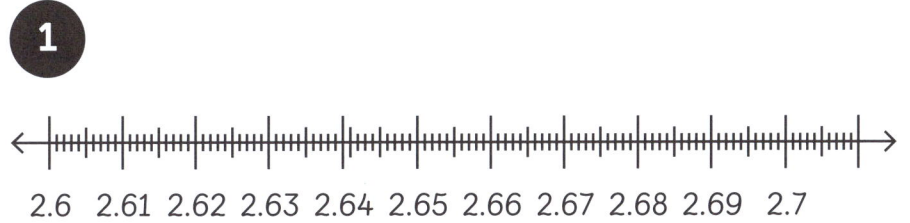

| | Rounded to the closest: | |
|---|---|---|
| | hundredths | tenths |
| 2.697 | | |

**2**

| | Rounded to the closest: | |
|---|---|---|
| | hundredths | tenths |
| 0.635 | | |

**3**

| | Rounded to the closest: | |
|---|---|---|
| | hundredths | tenths |
| 4.505 | | |

**4**

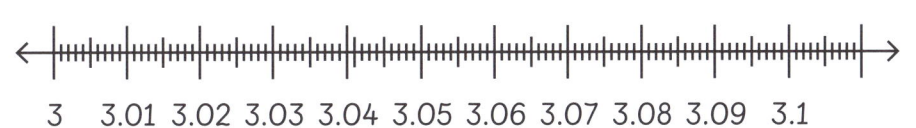

| | Rounded to the closest: | |
|---|---|---|
| | hundredths | tenths |
| 3.007 | | |

# Percentages

Lesson 16

## Starter

Oak wants to buy 300 stickers and she wants to get as many green stars as she can. Each of these sticker packs has multiple identical sheets.

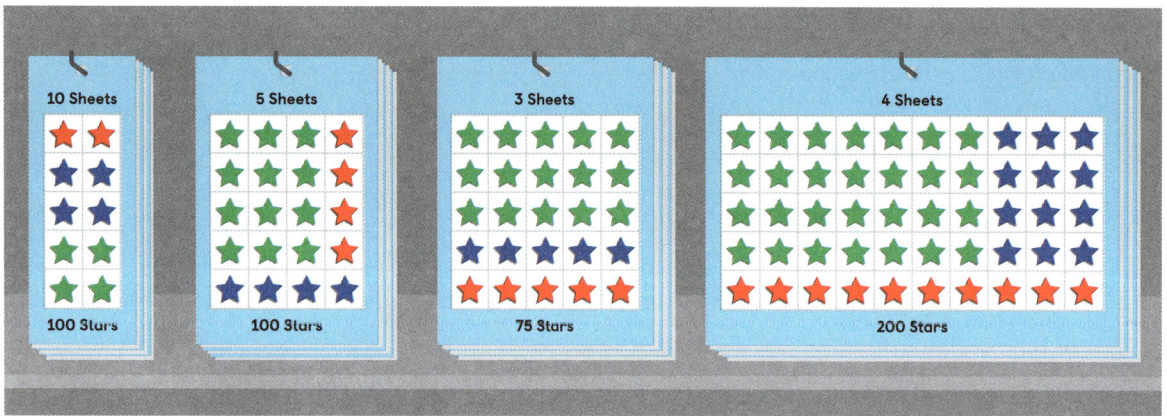

Which sticker packs should Oak buy?

## Example

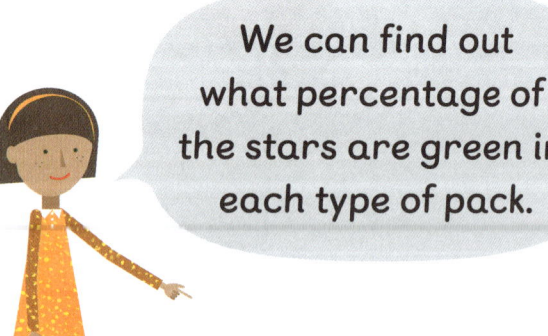

We can find out what percentage of the stars are green in each type of pack.

Percentage means how many out of 100.

first pack

second pack

third pack

fourth pack

In the first pack, 4 of 10 stars on each sheet are green.

$\frac{4}{10} = \frac{40}{100}$

We can say 40 percent of the stars are green.

We can use the % symbol for percent. We write 40 percent as 40%.

We can also show the percentages on a bar model like this.

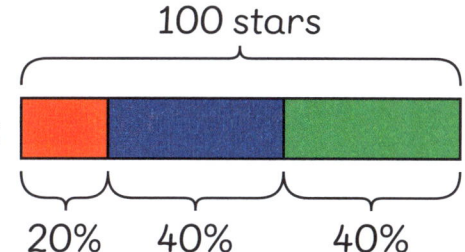

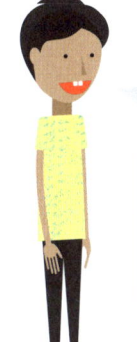

$\frac{12}{20}$ of the stars on each sheet are green in the second pack.
$\frac{12}{20} = \frac{60}{100}$
60% of the stars are green.

$\frac{15}{25}$ of the stars on each sheet are green in the third pack.
$\frac{15}{25} = \frac{60}{100}$
60% of the stars are green.

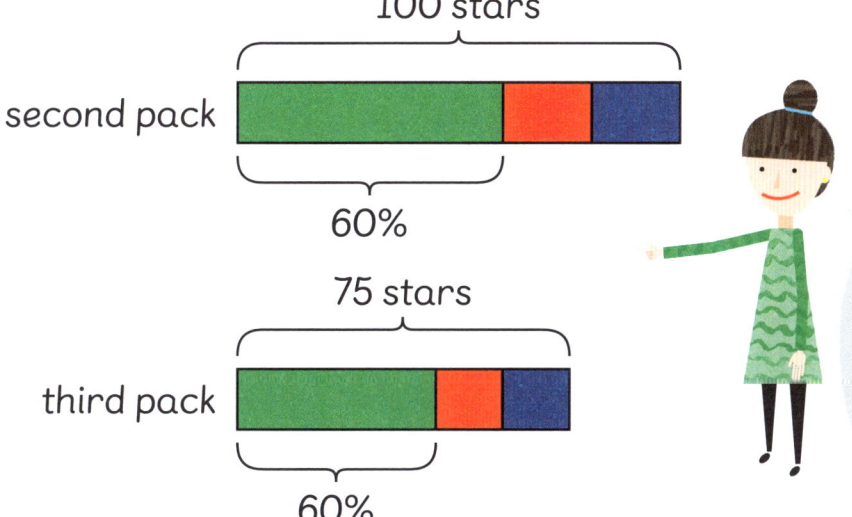

The second and the third packs don't have the same number of stars in their packs but 60% of the stars are green in both packs.

37

$\frac{28}{50}$ of the stars on each sheet are green in the fourth pack.

$\frac{28}{50} = \frac{56}{100}$

56% of the stars are green.

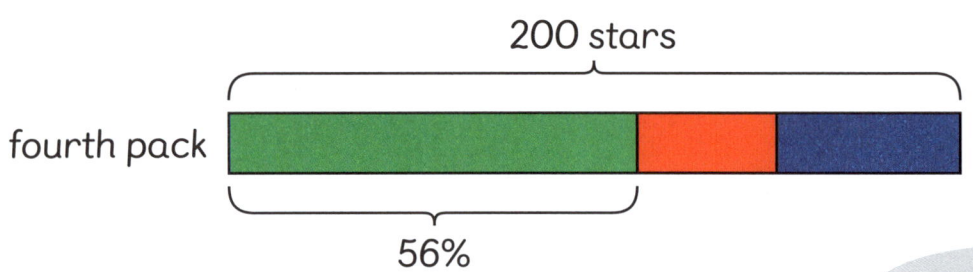

We can put all the information in a table.

The fourth pack has more stars than the other packs but it has a smaller percentage of green stars than the second and third packs.

| | | | |
|---|---|---|---|
| First pack | $\frac{4}{10}$ | $\frac{40}{100}$ | 40% |
| Second pack | $\frac{12}{20}$ | $\frac{60}{100}$ | 60% |
| Third pack | $\frac{15}{25}$ | $\frac{60}{100}$ | 60% |
| Fourth pack | $\frac{28}{50}$ | $\frac{56}{100}$ | 56% |

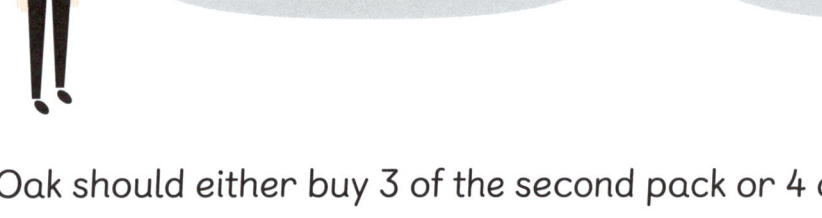

I think all the packs have the same percentage of red stars.

I am not sure Elliott is right. How can we check?

Oak should either buy 3 of the second pack or 4 of the third pack as they have the greatest percentage of green stars.

# Practice

**1** Look at the image in the Starter section and fill in the blanks.

|  | Percentage of red stars | Percentage of blue stars |
|---|---|---|
| First pack |  |  |
| Second pack |  |  |
| Third pack |  |  |
| Fourth pack |  |  |

Which 2 packs have the same percentages for each of the colours?

The _____ pack and the _____ pack both have equal percentages for each of the colours.

**2** In a box of 250 paper clips, 20% of them are red paper clips. How many of the paper clips are not red?

_____ paper clips are not red.

# Review and challenge

**1** Three different pizzas are shared equally by 4 friends. How much pizza does each friend get?

 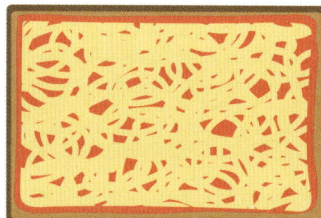 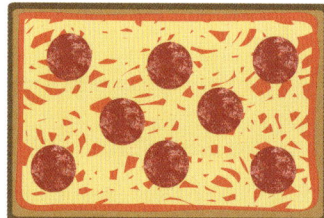

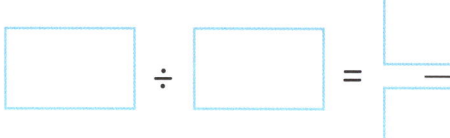 Each friend gets 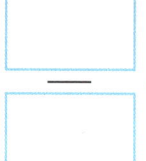 of a pizza.

**2** How much of the hexagons are shaded yellow?

(a)
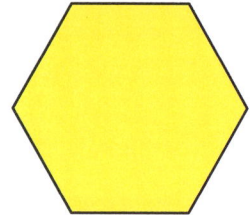 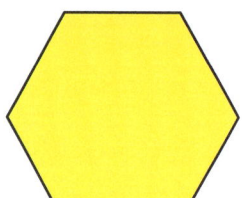 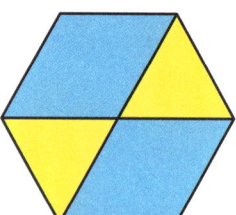

 of the hexagons are shaded yellow.

(b)
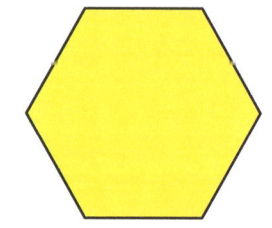  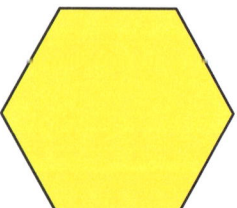 

 of the hexagons are shaded yellow.

**3** Fill in the blanks. Give your answers as improper fractions.

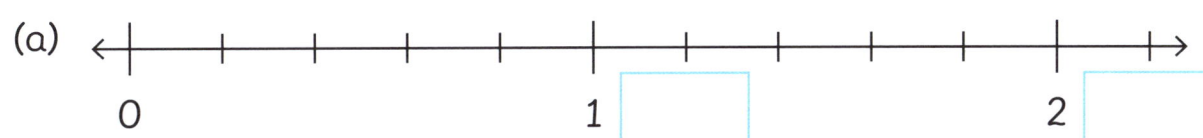

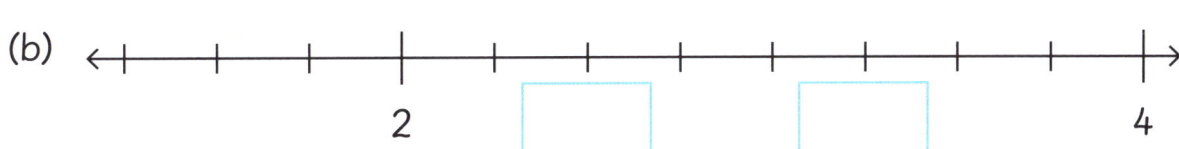

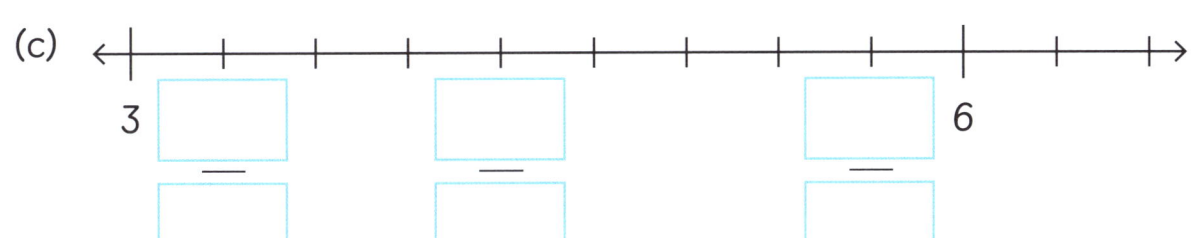

**4** Fill in the blanks. Give your answers as mixed numbers.

(a) $\dfrac{9}{7} = \boxed{\phantom{0}}\dfrac{\boxed{\phantom{0}}}{\boxed{\phantom{0}}}$

(b) $\dfrac{20}{3} = \boxed{\phantom{0}}\dfrac{\boxed{\phantom{0}}}{\boxed{\phantom{0}}}$

**5** Fill in the blanks. Give your answers as improper fractions.

(a) $1\dfrac{6}{7} = \dfrac{\boxed{\phantom{0}}}{\boxed{\phantom{0}}}$

(b) $9\dfrac{3}{4} = \dfrac{\boxed{\phantom{0}}}{\boxed{\phantom{0}}}$

6. There are 63 Year 5 pupils at the local school.
$\frac{2}{7}$ of the pupils wear glasses.

How many Year 5 pupils wear glasses?

[ ] Year 5 pupils wear glasses.

7. Match the equivalent fractions.

$\frac{4}{6}$ •   • $\frac{15}{27}$

$\frac{1}{2}$ •   • $\frac{2}{6}$

$\frac{7}{21}$ •   • $\frac{2}{3}$

$\frac{5}{9}$ •   • $\frac{7}{14}$

8. Fill in the blanks with > or <.

(a) $\frac{5}{6}$ [ ] $\frac{7}{8}$

(b) $\frac{5}{8}$ [ ] $\frac{7}{10}$

**9** Draw a bar model to solve the problem.

Jacob has 160 sports cards in his collection. Elliott has $\frac{5}{8}$ as many sports cards as Jacob has. Lulu has $\frac{3}{4}$ as many cards as Elliott has.

How many more cards does Jacob have than Lulu?

Jacob has ☐ more cards than Lulu.

**10** Add and give your answer as a mixed number.

(a) $\frac{3}{4} + \frac{5}{8} = \Box \frac{\Box}{\Box}$

(b) $\frac{1}{3} + \frac{8}{9} = \Box \frac{\Box}{\Box}$

**11** Add and give your answer as an improper fraction.

(a) $\frac{3}{4} + \frac{1}{2} = \frac{\Box}{\Box}$

(b) $\frac{1}{5} + \frac{9}{10} = \frac{\Box}{\Box}$

**12** Subtract and fill in the blanks.

(a) $\frac{2}{5} - \frac{1}{10} = \frac{4}{10} - \frac{1}{10} = \frac{\Box}{\Box}$

(b) $\frac{5}{8} - \frac{1}{4} = \frac{\Box}{\Box} - \frac{\Box}{\Box} = \frac{\Box}{\Box}$

**13** Shade the bars on the right and fill in the blanks.

$3 \times \dfrac{\square}{\square} = \square$

**14** Holly has the following recipe for making lemonade.
Rewrite the recipe so that the quantities are decimals of a litre instead of fractions of a litre.

*Lemonade Recipe*

$\frac{5}{8}$ l   water

$\frac{3}{8}$ l   lemon juice

$\frac{1}{4}$ l   white sugar

First, make a syrup by heating some of the water and the lemon juice on the stove.
When the syrup is hot, add all the sugar and mix until dissolved.
Set aside to let it cool. Mix the cooled syrup with the remainder of the water and mix well.

Serve cold.
Makes 4 servings.

☐ l of water

☐ l of white sugar

☐ l of lemon juice

**15** Fill in the blanks.

(a) 2.63 + 7 = ☐

(b) 0.94 + 0.18 = ☐

(c) 3.15 − 0.2 = ☐

(d) 3 − 2.22 = ☐

**16** Round the numbers to the closest hundredths and thousandths.

(a)
| | Rounded to the closest: | |
|---|---|---|
| | hundredths | tenths |
| 6.091 | | |

(b)
| | Rounded to the closest: | |
|---|---|---|
| | hundredths | tenths |
| 0.545 | | |

**17** What percentage of the apples are green?

☐ % of the apples are green.

# Answers

**Page 5** 1 (a) $2 \div 5 = \frac{2}{5}$ (b) $2 \div 4 = \frac{2}{4}$ 2 (a) $2 \div 3 = \frac{2}{3}$. $\frac{2}{3}$ of the circles are shaded in each colour. (b) $\frac{4}{6} = \frac{2}{3}$. Each friend gets $\frac{2}{3}$ of a candy strip.

**Page 7** 1 $3\frac{1}{2}$  2 $2\frac{1}{6}$  3 $1\frac{1}{3}$  4 $2\frac{1}{2}$

**Page 9** 1 (a) $\frac{6}{2}$ (b) $\frac{11}{4}$  2

**Page 11** 1 (a) There are 3 semi-circles. $\frac{3}{2} = 1\frac{1}{2}$ (b) There are 5 triangles. $\frac{5}{2} = 2\frac{1}{2}$  2 (a) $\frac{27}{12} = 2\frac{3}{12}$ (b) $1\frac{7}{11} = \frac{18}{11}$

**Page 13** 1 (a) $1\frac{3}{5} = \frac{8}{5}$ (b) $3\frac{1}{3} = \frac{10}{3}$ (c) $2\frac{3}{4} = \frac{11}{4}$  2 $5\frac{1}{6} = \frac{31}{6}$. Ravi ends up with 31 triangles.

**Page 15** 1 $\frac{1}{2} = \frac{2}{4} = \frac{3}{6} = \frac{4}{8}$  2 $\frac{1}{4} = \frac{2}{8} = \frac{3}{12} = \frac{4}{16}$  3 $\frac{1}{3} = \frac{2}{6} = \frac{3}{9} = \frac{4}{12}$  4 $\frac{1}{2} = \frac{2}{4}$

**Page 17**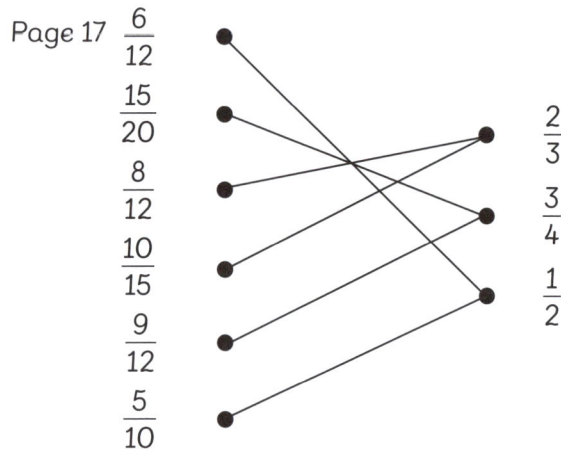

**Page 19** 1

2 Charles has read less than Emma. Emma has read more than Elliott. Elliott has read less than Charles. Emma has the least number of pages left to read. 3 Emma has read the most and Elliott has read the least.

**Page 22** 1 (a) Lulu scored 100 points. (b) Hannah and Lulu scored 250 points altogether.

**Page 23** 2 (a) £180 / £108 ; $180 \div 5 = 36$; $36 \times 3 = 108$. So far Ravi's brother has saved £108. (b) £108 / £90 ; $108 \div 6 = 18$; $18 \times 5 = 90$. His teammate has saved £90.

**Page 25**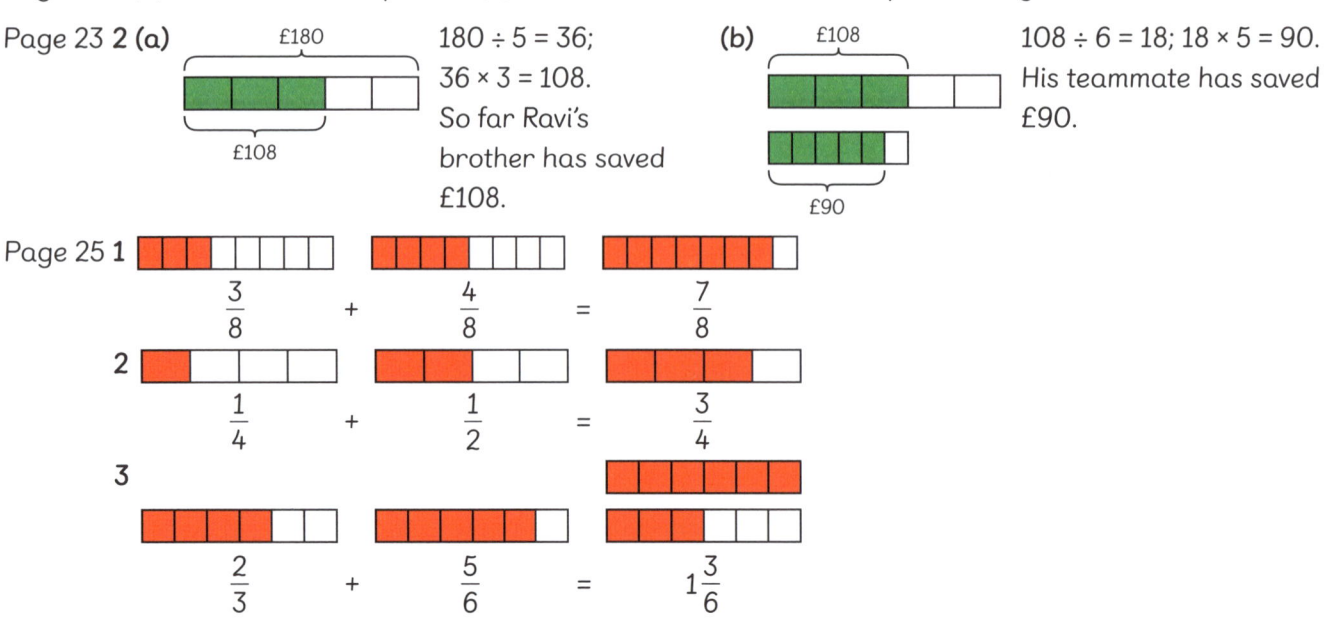

Page 27 **1**

$1\frac{3}{4} - \frac{7}{8} = \frac{7}{8}$

$1\frac{3}{5} - \frac{7}{10} = \frac{9}{10}$

$\frac{2}{3} - \frac{1}{6} = \frac{1}{2}$

**2** (a) $\frac{3}{4} - \frac{1}{2} = \frac{3}{4} - \frac{2}{4} = \frac{1}{4}$ (b) $1\frac{2}{3} - \frac{5}{6} = \frac{10}{6} - \frac{5}{6} = \frac{5}{6}$

Page 29 **1** $2 \times \frac{2}{5} = \frac{4}{5}$ **2** $3 \times \frac{2}{3} = \frac{6}{3}$ OR 2

**3** $7 \times \frac{3}{4} = \frac{21}{4}$ OR $5\frac{1}{4}$

Page 31 **1** $\frac{2}{5} = 0.4$; $\frac{1}{2} = 0.5$; $\frac{38}{100} = 0.38$; $\frac{38}{100}, \frac{2}{5}, \frac{1}{2}$ **2** $\frac{607}{1000} = 0.607$; $\frac{6}{100} = 0.06$; $\frac{6}{10} = 0.6$; $\frac{6}{100}, \frac{6}{10}, \frac{607}{1000}$

Page 33 **1** (a)
```
    7 . 5 3
  + 6 . 2 3
  ─────────
    1 3 . 7 6
```
(b)
```
    3 .¹2 8
  + 4 . 5 3
  ─────────
    7 . 8 1
```
(c)
```
    5 .¹5 4
  + 4 . 3 6
  ─────────
    9 . 9 0
```
(d)
```
   ¹9 .¹5 6
  +   9 . 4 4
  ─────────
   1 9 . 0 0
```

(e) $5.72 + 3 = 8.72$ (f) $0.83 + 0.18 = 1.01$ **2** (a)
```
    2 .⁶7̸ ¹2
  - 1 . 3 3
  ─────────
    1 . 3 9
```
(b)
```
   ⁷8̸ .⁴z̸² ¹4
  - 3 . 5 5
  ─────────
    4 . 6 9
```

(c) $3.15 - 0.2 = 2.95$ (d) $5 - 1.12 = 3.88$

Page 35 **1** 2.697

2.6  2.61  2.62  2.63  2.64  2.65  2.66  2.67  2.68  2.69  2.7

| | hundredths | tenths |
|---|---|---|
| 2.697 | 2.70 | 2.7 |

**2** 0.635

0.6  0.61  0.62  0.63  0.64  0.65  0.66  0.67  0.68  0.69  0.7

| | hundredths | tenths |
|---|---|---|
| 0.635 | 0.64 | 0.6 |

**3** 4.505

4.5  4.51  4.52  4.53  4.54  4.55  4.56  4.57  4.58  4.59  4.6

| | hundredths | tenths |
|---|---|---|
| 4.505 | 4.51 | 4.5 |

**4** 3.007

3  3.01  3.02  3.03  3.04  3.05  3.06  3.07  3.08  3.09  3.1

| | hundredths | tenths |
|---|---|---|
| 3.007 | 3.01 | 3.0 |

# Answers continued

**Page 39 1**

|              | Percentage of red stars | Percentage of blue stars |
|--------------|-------------------------|--------------------------|
| First pack   | 20%                     | 40%                      |
| Second pack  | 20%                     | 20%                      |
| Third pack   | 20%                     | 20%                      |
| Fourth pack  | 20%                     | 24%                      |

The second pack and the third pack both have equal percentages for each of the colours.
**2** 200 paper clips are not red.

**Page 40 1** $3 \div 4 = \frac{3}{4}$. Each friend gets $\frac{3}{4}$ of a pizza. **2 (a)** $2\frac{2}{6}$ of the hexagons are shaded yellow.
**(b)** $3\frac{2}{6}$ of the hexagons are shaded yellow.

**Page 41 3 (a)** 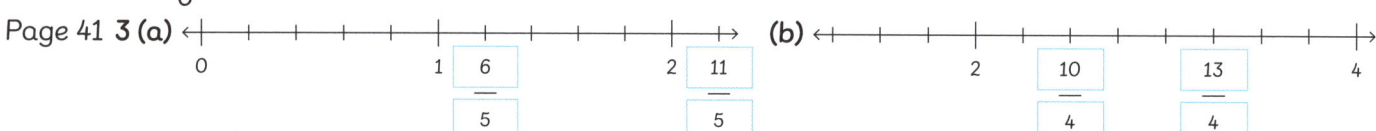 **(b)**

**(c)** 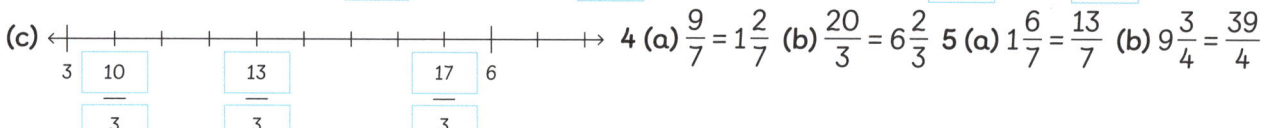 **4 (a)** $\frac{9}{7} = 1\frac{2}{7}$ **(b)** $\frac{20}{3} = 6\frac{2}{3}$ **5 (a)** $1\frac{6}{7} = \frac{13}{7}$ **(b)** $9\frac{3}{4} = \frac{39}{4}$

**Page 42 6** 18 Year 5 pupils wear glasses. **7** 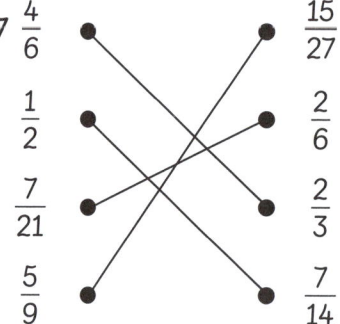 **8 (a)** $\frac{5}{6} < \frac{7}{8}$ **(b)** $\frac{5}{8} < \frac{7}{10}$

Matching: $\frac{4}{6} \leftrightarrow \frac{15}{27}$ (shown), $\frac{1}{2} \leftrightarrow \frac{2}{6}$, $\frac{7}{21} \leftrightarrow \frac{2}{3}$, $\frac{5}{9} \leftrightarrow \frac{7}{14}$

**Page 43 9**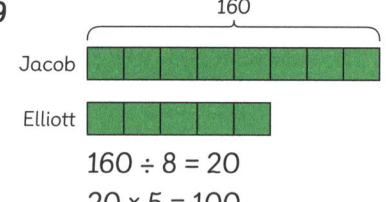

$160 \div 8 = 20$
$20 \times 5 = 100$

$100 \div 4 = 25$
$25 \times 3 = 75$

$160 - 75 = 85$
Jacob has 85 more cards than Lulu.

**10 (a)** $\frac{3}{4} + \frac{5}{8} = 1\frac{3}{8}$ **(b)** $\frac{1}{3} + \frac{8}{9} = 1\frac{2}{9}$ **11 (a)** $\frac{3}{4} + \frac{1}{2} = \frac{5}{4}$ **(b)** $\frac{1}{5} + \frac{9}{10} = \frac{11}{10}$

**12 (a)** $\frac{2}{5} - \frac{1}{10} = \frac{4}{10} - \frac{1}{10} = \frac{3}{10}$ **(b)** $\frac{5}{8} - \frac{1}{4} = \frac{5}{8} - \frac{2}{8} = \frac{3}{8}$

**Page 44 13** 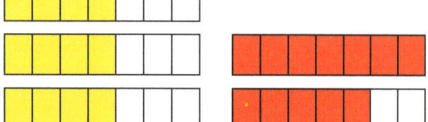 $3 \times \frac{4}{7} = 1\frac{5}{7}$ OR $\frac{12}{7}$ $

**14** 0.625 l of water; 0.375 l of lemon juice; 0.25 l of white sugar

**Page 45 15 (a)** $2.63 + 7 = 9.63$ **(b)** $0.94 + 0.18 = 1.12$ **(c)** $3.15 - 0.2 = 2.95$ **(d)** $3 - 2.22 = 0.78$

**16 (a)**

|       | hundredths | tenths |
|-------|------------|--------|
| 6.091 | 6.09       | 6.1    |

**(b)**

|       | hundredths | tenths |
|-------|------------|--------|
| 0.545 | 0.55       | 0.5    |

**17** 70% of the apples are green.